WHSmith

Progress Tests

English

Louis Fidge

Age 7–8
Year 3
Key Stage 2

Hachette UK's policy is to use papers that are natural, renewable and recyclable products and made from wood grown in sustainable forests. The logging and manufacturing processes are expected to conform to the environmental regulations of the country of origin.

Orders: please contact Bookpoint Ltd, 130 Milton Park, Abingdon, Oxon OX14 4SB. Telephone: (44) 01235 827720. Fax: (44) 01235 400454. Lines are open 9.00a.m.–5.00p.m., Monday to Saturday, with a 24-hour message answering service. Visit our website at www.hoddereducation.co.uk.

© Louis Fidge 2013
First published in 2013 exclusively for WH Smith by
Hodder Education
An Hachette UK Company
338 Euston Road
London NW1 3BH

Impression number   10 9 8 7 6 5 4 3 2 1
Year   2018 2017 2016 2015 2014 2013

Cover illustration by Oxford Designers and Illustrators Ltd
Illustrations by Fakenham Prepress Solutions, Fakenham, Norfolk NR21 8NN
Typeset in 16pt Folio by Fakenham Prepress Solutions, Fakenham, Norfolk NR21 8NN
Printed in [Production to complete]

A catalogue record for this title is available from the British Library.

ISBN: 978 1444 188 929

Introduction

How this book can help your child

Each *English Progress Test* book is designed for your child to complete on their own, but you may like to work with them for the first few tests to give them confidence and to be sure they can do the activities independently. This is particularly important for the first two books in the series (for ages 5–6, and 6–7). If children need extra support do provide it, perhaps by reading the reading passage together with them.

How to use this book

To get the most from this book:

- Try to choose a quiet place for doing the tests. Try to avoid other distractions (like having the TV on at the same time!).
- Don't let children struggle over words they don't know. Let them have a good go first of all, but if they simply cannot work out the word, tell them what it is.
- Don't get your child to do too much at once. A 'little and often' approach is a good way to start.
- Your child should work systematically through the book test by test.
- Do reward your child with lots of praise and encouragement. Be positive. Don't just comment on mistakes.

- Talk to your child about what they have learnt and what they can do.
- When they have read the reading passage, get them to check their understanding by working through the questions on the page opposite.
- The first section (**Checking understanding**) is made up of comprehension questions. The answers to these are always to be found in the text. (Some questions may need a bit of thinking about than others!)
- The second section (**Sentences**) checks children's understanding of sentence structure (grammar and punctuation etc.) linked to the passage.
- The third section (**Words**) checks children's understanding of spelling and vocabulary linked to the passage.
- Involve your child in marking the tests and talk together about any incorrect answers. Be sensitive and draw more attention to those that were correct, asking your child to tell you how they tackled the question and what they found difficult about it.
- When the marks for the test are added up, the results may be recorded on the record sheet (on the inside back cover). This will give you and the children a sense of how well they are doing.

One day a crow picked up a piece of cheese from the ground in its beak. It flew up into a tree with the cheese. A hungry fox came by and saw the crow with the cheese in its beak.

The fox wanted to make the crow let go of the cheese. The fox was very crafty. He had a plan. He looked up and smiled at the crow.

'What a beautiful bird you are,' he said. The crow said nothing.

'What lovely feathers you've got,' the fox said. Again the crow said nothing.

'Have you got a beautiful voice?' the fox asked. The crow wanted to show the fox what a lovely voice she had, so she opened her beak to sing. She let go of the cheese and it fell to the ground.

The fox ate it greedily. 'Thank you,' said the fox. He ran off laughing to himself. 'What a clever fellow I am,' he thought to himself.

A fable by Aesop

Checking understanding

Answer these questions.

1. What did the crow pick up in its beak? — *Cheese*
2. Where did it fly to with the cheese? — *tree*
3. Who saw the crow with the cheese? — *The fox*
4. What did the fox want to make the crow do? — *let go of the cheese*
5. What word means *clever* or *sly*? — *crafty*
6. What was the first thing the fox said to the crow? — *He had a plan*
7. What was the second thing he said? — *He looked up and smiled at the crow*
8. What question did the fox ask the crow? — *What a beautiful bird*
9. Why did the crow open her beak to sing? — *You are to show her lovely voice she had*
10. What happened when the crow opened her beak? — *She let go of the cheese*

Sentences

Complete each sentence with a suitable verb.

11. The crow ___flew___ up into the tree.
12. The crow ___opened___ her beak to sing.

Words

Find a word containing:

13. 'ie' ___piece___   14. 'ful' ___beautiful___   15. 'augh' ___laughing___

Mark your answers. How well did you do?

I scored __12__ out of 15.

Johnny Appleseed loved nature. Everywhere he went he carried a bag of apple seeds and planted them. He told everyone how important it was to look after the world.

Johnny had no home of his own. He went from place to place, planting his apple seeds. But Johnny made lots of friends. They gave him food and shelter. Even the animals loved Johnny.

One winter night, after sunset, Johnny became ill and fainted. Just then a wild grizzly bear came by in the snow. The bear did not attack Johnny. It wandered away.

Later, some of Johnny's friends wondered where Johnny was. They began to search the woods for him. They saw his footprints in the snow and followed them until they found him. His friends took Johnny home and cared for him until he was well again.

As soon as he had recovered, Johnny set off on his journeys once again, planting apple seeds wherever he went.

Checking understanding

Write T (true) or F (false) after each sentence.

1. Johnny Appleseed loved nature. *true*
2. Everywhere he went he carried a bag of pear seeds. *false*
3. Everywhere he went, Johnny planted apple seeds. *true*
4. Johnny lived in a hut in the woods. *false*
5. Johnny's friends gave him food and shelter. *true*
6. Johnny became ill in the woods one summer evening. *false*
7. A wild grizzly bear came by and found Johnny in the snow. *false* ✗
8. The bear did not attack Johnny. *true*
9. Johnny's friends followed the bear's footprints in the snow. *false*
10. Johnny's friends cared for him until he was well again. *true*

Sentences

Write each sentence again, and punctuate it correctly.

11. everywhere he went johnny planted apple seeds

    Everywhere Johnny went he planted apple seeds

12. did johnny appleseed love nature

    Johnny Appleseed loved nature

Words

Do these word sums and make some compound words.

13. foot + prints = *footprints*
14. every + where = *everywhere*
15. sun + set = *sunset*

Mark your answers. How well did you do?

I scored __15__ out of 15.

Betty

Betty bought a bit of butter.
Betty said, 'My butter's bitter.
If I put it in my batter,
It will make my batter bitter.
I'd better buy some better butter.'
So she bought a bit of butter
Better than her bitter butter.
When she put it in her batter,
It made Betty's batter better.

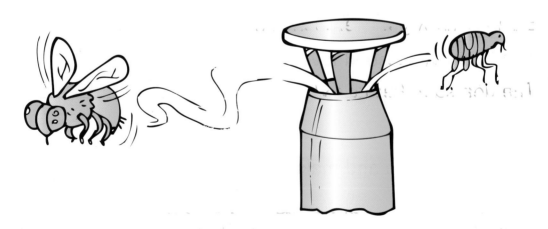

A fly and a flea

A fly and a flea in a flue
Were wondering what they should do.
Said the fly, 'Let us flee!'
Said the flea, 'Let us fly!'
So they flew through the flaw in the flue!

Checking understanding

Answer these questions.

1. Who bought a bit of butter?   *Betty* ✓
2. What was wrong with her bit of butter?   *it was bitter* ✓
3. What did she want to put some butter in?   *batter* ✓
4. Did Betty buy some better butter?   *Yes* ✓
5. When she put her better butter in her batter, did it make her batter better or worse?   *better* ✓
6. Where were the fly and the flea?   *flue* ✓
7. What were they wondering?   *should do* ✓
8. What did the fly say?   *Let us flee* ✓
9. What did the flea say?   *Let us fly* ✓
10. Where did they fly?   *into the flue* ✓

Sentences

Put in the missing speech marks in these sentences.

11. Betty said, "My batter is bitter." ✗
12. The fly said, "Let us flee!" ✓
13. The flea said, "Let us fly!" ✓

Words

14. Write four words beginning with 'b' from the first rhyme:

    bought ✓   *bit* ✓   *butter* ✓   *Betty* ✓

15. Write four words beginning with 'fl' from the second rhyme:

    fly ✓   *flea* ✓   *flue* ✓   *flee*

Mark your answers. How well did you do?

I scored *14* out of 15.

What you need

two medium-sized
bananas

a mixing bowl

a fork

two cups of
cold milk

four scoops of
vanilla ice cream

two tall glasses

What to do

- Peel the bananas.

- Put the bananas in the mixing bowl.

- Mash them with the fork.

- Add the milk.

- Stir until the mixture is smooth.

- Add the ice cream and mix it in.

- Serve up your milkshakes in your glasses.

Checking understanding

Answer these questions.

1 Do you need hot or cold milk? _cold_ ✓

2 How many medium-sized bananas do you need? _two_ ✓

3 How many scoops of vanilla ice cream do you need? _four_ ✓

4 What do you do first? ✓ _peel the bananas_

5 Where do you put the peeled bananas? _bowl_ ✓

6 What do you use the fork for? _with the fork. Mash the bananas_

7 What do you add after you have mashed the bananas? _Add the milk_

8 What do you do to the mixture to make it smooth? _stir_ ✓

9 What is the last thing you add? _ice cream_ ✓

10 What do you put your milkshakes into? _glasses_ ✓

Sentences

Complete each sentence with a sensible adjective.

11 You need two cups of _cold_ milk. ✓

12 You need two _medium-sized_ bananas. ✓

13 You need two _tall_ glasses. ✓

Words

Find a word containing:

14 'ir' _stir_ ✓

15 'er' _serve_ ✓

> **Mark your answers. How well did you do?**
>
> I scored _15_ out of 15.

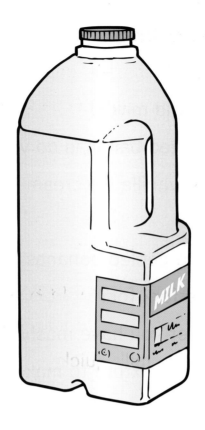

A cow eats grass to help her make milk.

⬇

The farmer milks the cow with a machine.

⬇

A tanker comes to the farm to collect the milk.

⬇

The tanker takes the milk to the dairy.

⬇

At the dairy, the milk is heated up and cooled down quickly. This kills any germs.

⬇

The milk is put into plastic bottles or cartons.

⬇

It is then taken to the shop to be sold.

Checking understanding

Choose the best word to fill in each gap.

1. We get _milk_ (milk, silk) from a cow.
2. A cow eats _grass_ (green, grass) to help her make milk.
3. The farmer milks the cow with a _machine_ (match, machine).
4. A _tanker_ (tank, tanker) collects the milk from the farm.
5. The tanker takes the milk to the _dairy_ (dairy, diary).
6. The milk is _heated_ (beaten, heated up).
7. Then the milk is _cooled_ (cooled, pooled) down quickly.
8. Heating and cooling the milk quickly _kills_ (kills, spills) any germs.
9. The milk is put into bottles or _cartons_ (cartons, cartoons).
10. The milk is taken to the _shop_ (chop, shop) to be sold.

Sentences

Complete each sentence with a sensible noun.

11. A _farmer_ keeps cows on a farm.
12. Milk is put into bottles in a _shop_ . Dairy
13. We can buy milk from a _shop_ .

Words

14. Find a word in which the 'ch' sounds like 'sh': _shop_
15. Find a word ending with 'ic': _plastic_

Mark your answers. How well did you do?

I scored _13_ out of 15.

A   is for apples, so tasty to munch,

B   is for bananas, they hang in a bunch.

C   is for cake, with icing so white,

D   is for doughnuts, so soft to bite.

E   is for eggs, fried in a pan,

F   is for fish, catch it if you can!

G   is for ginger, tangy to eat,

H   is for ham, my favourite meat.

I   is for ice cream, soft and cold,

J   is for jelly from a mould.

K   is for ketchup in a jar,

L   is for lemon, too sour by far!

M is for mangoes in a sack,

N is for nuts that are hard to crack.

Checking understanding

Answer these questions.

1. What are tasty to munch?   _apples_ ✓
2. What has white icing on it?   _cake_ ✓
3. What's soft and cold?   _ice cream_ ✓
4. What is too sour?   _lemon_ ✓
5. What are hard to crack?   _nuts_ ✓
6. What are fried in a pan?   _eggs_ ✓
7. What fruit comes in a sack?   _mangoes_ ✓
8. What fruit comes in a bunch?   _bananas_ ✓
9. What is from a mould?   _jelly_ ✓
10. What are soft to bite?   _doughnuts_ ✓

Sentences

Write the two lines that end with exclamation marks.

11. _I love bananas!_ ✓
12. _lemon's are sour!_ ✓

Words

Write these foods in alphabetical order:

13. biscuit apricot crisps   _Apricot biscuit crisps_ ✓
14. jam fig melon grape   _fig grape jam melon_ ✓
15. onion rice toast pear   _onion pear rice toast_ ✓

Mark your answers. How well did you do?

I scored _13_ out of 15.

15

Once upon a time there was a poor boy called Chang, who liked to draw. One day, an old man with a long white beard appeared. He gave Chang a pencil. 'Use this pencil to draw pictures for poor people,' the old man said.

Chang saw a poor man cutting wood. 'You need a sharp axe,' Chang said. So he drew an axe and it changed into a real axe. 'Thank you. You are very kind,' the man said to Chang.

Next he saw a poor woman carrying a load of vegetables to market. 'You need a wheelbarrow,' Chang said. So he drew a wheelbarrow and it changed into a real wheelbarrow. 'Thank you. You are very kind,' the woman said to Chang.

Soon the king heard about Chang's magic pencil. 'Draw me a sack of gold,' the king ordered Chang.
Chang said, 'You are already rich. You don't need any more gold.' The king was angry and threw Chang into prison. Chang drew a key, unlocked the prison door and walked out.

The king chased Chang, so Chang drew a horse and galloped away to safety.

A story from China

Checking understanding

Choose the best word to fill in each gap.

1. Chang liked to _draw_ (draw, paint).
2. An old man gave Chang a _pencil_ (pen, pencil).
3. Chang saw a poor man cutting _wood_ (potatoes, wood).
4. Chang saw a poor woman carrying _vegetables_ (fruit, vegetables).
5. Chang drew a _wheelbarrow_ (cart, wheelbarrow) for the woman.
6. The _King_ (king, queen) heard about Chang's magic pencil.
7. The king ordered Chang to draw him a sack of _gold_ (gold, carrots).
8. Chang told the king he was already _rich_ (rich, poor).
9. The king threw Chang into _prison_ (jail, prison).
10. Chang drew a _key_ (kite, key) to unlock the prison door.

Sentences

The words in these sentences are in the wrong order.
Write the sentences correctly.

11. boy. kind Chang was a _Chang was a kind boy._
12. old man Chang beard. saw an with a long white
Chang saw a old man with an long white beard.

Words

13. Change the 'dr' in 'draw' to 'str' to make something you drink through: _straw_
14. Change the 'p' in 'poor' to 'd' to make something you open: _door_
15. Change the 'l' in 'load' to 'r' to make something you drive on: _road_

Mark your answers. How well did you do?

I scored _15_ out of 15.

17

Pandas come from China. They are very rare animals. There are not many pandas left in the world, so they have to be protected.

A panda is very large, like a big bear. It has a round face, small ears and a black patch around each eye. It has a furry black and white coat. Its fur is very thick and helps keep it warm in cold weather. A panda's coat is also waterproof and keeps out the rain.

A panda has big teeth and strong jaws. It eats lots of bamboo. This is a kind of woody plant and is very tough. Pandas spend about fourteen hours a day eating! The rest of the time they spend sleeping!

Baby pandas are called cubs. They are tiny when they are born. The mother panda looks after the cubs. When the cubs are about a year and a half they are old enough to live on their own.

Checking understanding

Answer these questions with 'yes' or 'no'.

1. Do pandas come from China? *yes* ✓
2. Are there lots of pandas? *no* ✓
3. Is a panda a large animal? *yes* ✓
4. Does a panda have large ears? *no* ✓
5. Is a panda's fur very thick? *yes* ✓
6. Does a panda's fur keep out the rain? *yes* ✓
7. Does a panda have strong jaws? *yes* ✓
8. Do pandas spend only four hours a day eating? *no* ✓
9. Do pandas eat bamboo? *yes* ✓
10. Is a baby panda called a calf? *no* ✓

Sentences

Complete each sentence with a sensible adjective.

11. Pandas are *tiny* when they are born. ✓
12. A panda has a *black* patch around each eye. ✓
13. A panda's fur is *thick* so it keeps the panda warm. ✓

Words

14. Find a word that ends with 'ur': *fur* ✓
15. Find a word that ends with 'ough': *enough* ✓

Mark your answers. How well did you do?

I scored *15* out of 15.

19

Hubble bubble muddy puddle
Muddy puddle in the rain.
The rain makes puddles nice and deep
Good to splash in with your feet.

Hubble bubble muddy puddle
Muddy puddle in the rain.
Take your umbrella, put on your coat,
Take your wellies and a sailing boat.

Hubble bubble muddy puddle
Muddy puddle in the rain.
Splosh go the cars as they whoosh by.
So many black clouds in the sky.

Hubble bubble muddy puddle
Muddy puddle in the rain.
Feed the ducks with a loaf of bread.
Then go home to a nice warm bed.

Checking understanding

Choose the best word to fill in each gap.

1. The rain makes puddles nice and _deep_ (damp, deep).
2. Puddles are good to _splash_ (splash, spin) in with your feet.
3. An umbrella keeps you _dry_ (dry, wet).
4. We wear a _coat_ (boat, coat) when it rains.
5. We wear _wellies_ (wheels, wellies) when it rains.
6. We can sail a _boat_ (goat, boat) in deep puddles.
7. The cars _whoosh_ (wish, whoosh) by.
8. When it rains there are _black_ (white, black) clouds in the sky.
9. We feed the ducks with a loaf of _bread_ (bread, head).
10. After we feed the ducks we go home to a warm _bed_ (red, bed).

Sentences

Write each sentence again, and punctuate it correctly.

11. when it rains it makes puddles   _When it rains, it makes puddle_
12. can i borrow your umbrella   _can i borrow your umbrella?_
13. i like deep muddy puddles   _like deep, muddy puddles!_

Words

Write the word that rhymes with:

14. by _sky_
15. bread _bed_

Mark your answers. How well did you do?

I scored _15_ out of 15.

One day Jo and her mum went shopping. They went into the shoe shop. Jo saw some lovely trainers. They were just what she wanted. Jo tried them on. They fitted perfectly. Her mum said she could have them because her old trainers were worn out. As Jo went home she felt very excited.

The first thing Jo did when she got home was to put on her new trainers. As she did so she felt very odd. She started to float in the air. At first she felt a bit dizzy. Then she started to fly like a bird. The trainers were magic!

She flew up and up and up, high in the sky. When she looked down, everything looked smaller – the cars looked like beetles and the people looked as small as ants. Her house looked like a little box. Jo decided to fly off to have some adventures.

Checking understanding

Answer these questions.

1. What shop did Jo and her mum go into? *shoe shop* ✓
2. What did Jo buy in the shop? *trainers* ✓
3. Did the trainers fit Jo? *yes* ✓
4. What was wrong with Jo's old trainers? *worn out* ✓
5. What was the first thing Jo did when she got home? *put on her trainers* ✓
6. What happened when she put on her trainers? *she started to fly* ✓
7. Did everything look bigger or smaller when she was in the sky? *smaller* ✓
8. What did the cars look like? *beetles* ✓
9. What did people look like? *ants* ✓
10. What did her house look like? *box* ✓

Sentences

Complete each sentence with a sensible adjective about feelings.

11. On her way home Jo felt *excited*. ✓
12. When Jo put on her new trainers she felt *odd*. ✓
13. When Jo started to float in the air she felt *dizzy*. ✓

Words

Fill in the missing letter in each word:

14. ma_g_ic
15. ex_c_ited

Mark your answers. How well did you do?

I scored _15_ out of 15.

23

This story is written in the form of a play.

Narrator: It was a lovely hot summer's day. Cara and Alfie went to the beach. They took a picnic with them in a basket. The tide was out so there was lots of sand to play on.

Cara: This looks like a nice spot. Let's stop here.
Alfie: It's fine. There aren't too many people.
Cara: I'll put our towels down to sit on.
Alfie: I'll get out our buckets and spades.

Narrator: Cara and Alfie put on their swimming costumes. They left their clothes on the towels with their picnic basket. Then they had fun building sandcastles. When they got hot, they decided to go into the sea.

Alfie: Stop splashing me, Cara!
Cara: Look! I can swim underwater!
Alfie: Watch me jump the waves!

Narrator: The children had lots of fun in the water – but they did not notice that the tide was coming in very fast. A big wave washed their clothes and picnic into the sea. Their clothes and picnic basket floated on the water near the children.

Cara: Oh no! Look at our clothes!
Alfie: Look at our picnic!

Narrator: The children quickly grabbed their wet clothes and picnic basket and ran out of the water. They took everything further up the beach to dry.

Cara: Luckily the sun's strong. It will soon dry our clothes.
Alfie: Yes – but it won't dry our sandwiches. They are all soggy!

Checking understanding

Write T (true) or F (false) after each sentence.

1. It was a lovely hot summer's day.   _true_
2. There were lots of people on the beach.   _false_
3. Cara and Alfie left their clothes on their towels.   _true_
4. The children decided to go in the sea straightaway.   _F_
5. Alfie splashed Cara.   _F_
6. Cara can swim underwater.   _T_
7. A big wave washed their clothes and picnic into the sea.   _T_
8. The picnic basket sank.   _F_
9. The children took everything further up the beach to dry.   _T_
10. Alfie said that the sun would soon dry their clothes.   _F_

Sentences

Put in the missing speech marks in these sentences.

11. Cara said, "Look! I can swim underwater!"
12. "Watch me jump the waves!" Alfie shouted.
13. Cara said, "The sun will soon dry our clothes."

Words

14. Change the 'b' in 'beach' to 'p' to make something to eat:
    peach
15. Change the 'st' in 'strong' to 'w' to make something not right:
    wrong

Mark your answers. How well did you do?

I scored 15 out of 15.

25

Andy Hay

One day a boy called Andy Hay
Went to the seaside on holiday.
He went for a swim in the big blue bay
And there he met a shark at play.
The shark ate him before you could say –
Oh what a pity – poor Andy Hay!

Algy met a bear

Algy met a bear,
The bear met Algy,
The bear grew bulgy –
The bulge was Algy.

Way down south

Way down south where bananas grow,
A grasshopper stood on an elephant's toe.
The elephant said, with tears in his eyes,
'Why don't you pick on somebody your own size?'

Checking understanding

Answer these questions.

1. Who is the first rhyme about? _Andy_ ✓
2. Where did he go for a swim? _The seaside_ ✓
3. What did he meet while he was swimming? _A shark_ ✓
4. What did the shark do to Andy? _The shark ate him_ ✓
5. Who is the second rhyme about? _Algy_ ✓
6. Who did Algy meet? _The bear_ ✓
7. What did the bear do to Algy? _bulge_ ✓
8. What grow down south? _bananas_ ✓
9. Where did the grasshopper stand? _on the elephant's toe_ ✓
10. What did the elephant say to the grasshopper? _he said why don't you pick on somebody your own size_ ✓

Sentences

The words in these sentences are in the wrong order.

Write the sentences correctly.

11. in the bay for a Andy went swim. _Andy in the bay for a swim_
12. an elephant's toe. A stood grasshopper on

A grasshopper stood on an elephant's toe. ✓

Words

Match one of these animals to each description:
shark, grasshopper, bear

13. A small insect that uses its long back legs to jump. _grasshopper_ ✓
14. A very big, heavy, wild animal. _bear_ ✓
15. A very large sea fish that has many sharp teeth. _shark_ ✓

Mark your answers. How well did you do?

I scored _14_ out of 15.

When Ben went down for his breakfast he could hear a funny noise in the kitchen. When he opened the door he was amazed to see a DRAGON. It had scales and long legs with claws. Its teeth were sharp and pointed. Although Ben knew dragons were fierce creatures, this dragon looked rather friendly.

'Hello!' the dragon said in a deep voice. 'I'm hungry so I dropped in for breakfast.' He puffed out a few clouds of smoke from his nostrils.

'Would you like some eggs?' Ben asked. 'Yes, please,' said the dragon. Before Ben could cook them, the dragon ate the lot – shells and all.

'How about some baked beans?' Ben asked. 'Yes, please,' said the dragon. Before Ben could open the tin, the dragon grabbed hold of it and swallowed it whole in one mouthful.

Ben could see that the dragon was starving. 'Do you like bread?' Ben asked. 'Yes, I do,' said the dragon. 'I like it toasted.' Before Ben could pop some slices into the toaster, the dragon breathed a big flame of fire over the bread and toasted the whole loaf. He then popped the whole toasted loaf into his mouth.

'What about some orange juice?' Ben asked. 'Yes, I'm very thirsty,' said the dragon. There was a loud hiss as he poured the carton of juice down his throat.

By now the dragon was full. 'Well, I must be on my way. Thanks for breakfast!' said the dragon. He got up, flapped his wings and flew off through the open window.

Ben wondered where the dragon was going for lunch.

Checking understanding

Answer these questions.

1. Where did Ben hear a funny noise when he went down for breakfast? *Kitchen*
2. What did he find in the kitchen? *DRACTON*
3. What were the dragon's teeth like? *pointed*
4. What did the dragon puff out of his nostrils? *smoke*
5. What did the dragon eat first? *eggs*
6. How did the dragon eat the baked beans? *swallowed it whole*
7. Did the dragon eat a few slices of bread or the whole loaf? *The bread*
8. What noise was there when the dragon drank the orange juice? *loud hiss*
9. When he flew through the window, what did the dragon flap? *his wings*
10. What did Ben wonder at the end of the story? *The dragon's lunch*

Sentences

Fill in each gap with a sensible adjective.

11. The dragon had _long_ legs.
12. The dragon had a _deep_ voice.
13. The dragon flew off through the _open_ window.

Words

14. Change the 'sc' in 'scales' to 'wh' to make some big sea animals: _whales_
15. Add 'c' to the beginning of 'loud' to make something that floats in the sky: _cloud_

Mark your answers. How well did you do?

I scored ____ out of 15.

A number rhyme

Number one, stick out your tongue.

Number two, touch your shoe.

Number three, bend your knee.

Number four, sit on the floor.

Number five, learn to jive.

Number six, lick your lips.

Number seven, point up to heaven.

Number eight, shut the gate.

Number nine, feel your spine.

Number ten, do it again!

Checking understanding

Answer these questions.

1 Where do you sit for number four? *the floor*

2 What do you shut for number eight? *the gate*

3 What do you lick for number six? *the lips*

4 What do you touch for number two? *your shoe*

5 What do you feel for number nine? *feel your spine*

6 What do you bend for number three? *Your knee*

7 What dance do you learn for number five? *to jive*

8 Where do you point for number seven? *to heaven*

9 Which line tells you to do something rude? *line eight*

10 How many lines are there in this rhyme? *ten*

Sentences

11 Write the first line and underline the two punctuation marks in it.

Number one, stick out your tongue.

12 Write the line that ends with an exclamation mark.

Number ten, do it again!

Words

Write the word that rhymes with:

13 two *shoe*   14 four *your*   15 eight *gate*

> ## Mark your answers. How well did you do?
>
> I scored ____ out of 15.

Trees are the biggest living things in the world. Many live longer than any other living thing.

The main part of a tree is its trunk. There is bark around the outside of the trunk. Bark stops the tree from getting too hot or too cold.

The roots of a tree go a long way into the ground. They help the tree to stand up and they soak up water from the ground for the tree.

Branches grow from the trunk of the tree. Smaller branches are called twigs.

Leaves on the tree make food for the tree. They make this food from water and a gas in the air called carbon dioxide. Trees need light to help make their food.

Many trees have flowers. Insects such as bees carry pollen from one flower to another. This makes seeds for new trees. Some trees grow fruit. Inside the fruit are seeds.

When a tree is cut down, you can count the rings and see how old it is. One ring stands for one year.

Lots of animals and insects make their homes in trees. We make things from the wood from trees. We also eat the fruit from fruit trees.

Checking understanding

Write T (true) or F (false) after each sentence.

1. Trees are the biggest living things in the world. _____

2. The main part of a tree is its trunk. _____

3. Bark stops the tree from getting wet. _____

4. The roots of a tree grow above the ground. _____

5. Roots soak up water from the ground for the tree. _____

6. Branches grow from the roots of the tree. _____

7. Leaves on the tree make food for the tree. _____

8. Trees need darkness to help make their food. _____

9. Many trees have flowers. _____

10. You can count the rings on the trunk to see how old the tree is. _____

Sentences

Fill in each gap with a sensible verb.

11. Branches _____ from the trunk of the tree.

12. Insects _____ pollen from one flower to another.

13. We _____ the fruit from fruit trees.

Words

Write in the missing plurals:

14. one branch but two _____   15. one leaf but two _____

Mark your answers. How well did you do?

I scored ____ out of 15.

Peg Leg was the captain of the bad ship Thunderbolt. He was very frightening to look at. He terrified even the bravest pirates.

Peg Leg looked like a barrel. He wore a spotted scarf on his head. He had bushy black eyebrows. He had eyes that stuck out. His red face always looked angry. His long black beard made him look wild. A scar ran down his left cheek.

But the very worst thing about Peg Leg was his right leg, which was short and thick. His peg leg was made from an old ship's timber. Whenever he walked on the deck his leg made a frightening noise – Bang! Bang! Bang!

In his belt, Peg Leg carried a sharp sword and a knife with a curved blade.

One dark night, Peg Leg decided to set sail. 'We'll look for a rich cargo ship and blow her to pieces, me hearties!' he snarled at his crew. The ship set sail out of the harbour and into the night.

Checking understanding

Choose the best word to fill in each gap.

1. Peg Leg was the captain of the _____ (Thunderbolt, Lightning).

2. Peg Leg looked like a _____ (bulldog, barrel).

3. His eyes _____ (stuck, popped) out.

4. Peg Leg's long black _____ (beard, eyebrows) made him look wild.

5. A scar ran down his _____ (right, left) cheek.

6. Peg Leg's right leg was _____ (long, short) and thick.

7. His peg leg was made from an old ship's _____ (anchor, timber).

8. His leg made a _____ (fearsome, frightening) noise.

9. Peg Leg carried a sharp _____ (knife, sword).

10. One _____ (night, morning) the ship set sail.

Sentences

Fill in each gap with a sensible noun.

11. Peg Leg was the _____ of the Thunderbolt.

12. Peg Leg wore a spotted _____ on his head.

Words

Match one of these words to each description: pirate, harbour, sword

13. a place for boats and ships to stay _____

14. someone on a ship, who attacks and robs other ships _____

15. a weapon like a knife, with a long sharp blade _____

Mark your answers. How well did you do?

I scored ____ out of 15.

What is pink?

What is pink? A rose is pink
By the fountain's brink.
What is red? A poppy's red
In its barley bed.
What is blue? The sky is blue
Where the clouds float through.
What is white? A swan is white
Sailing in the light.
What is yellow? Pears are yellow,
Rich, ripe and mellow.
What is green? The grass is green,
With small flowers in between.
What is violet? Clouds are violet
In the summer twilight.
What is orange?
Why, an orange is orange,
Just an orange!

Christina Rossetti

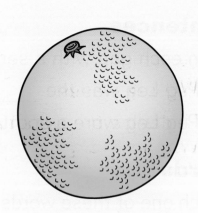

Checking understanding

Choose the best word to fill in each gap.

1 A _____ (rose, poppy) is pink.

2 A _____ (rose, poppy) is red.

3 The sky is blue where the _____ (sun, clouds) float through.

4 A swan is white _____ (swimming, sailing) in the light.

5 _____ (Pears, Apples) are yellow.

6 The grass is green, with small _____ (plants, flowers) in between.

7 Clouds are violet in the summer _____ (night, twilight).

8 An orange is _____ (yellow, orange).

9 _____ (Eight, Ten) colours are mentioned in the poem.

10 There are _____ (seventeen, twenty) lines in the poem.

Sentences

11 Underline the question mark in this sentence:
What is orange?

12 Underline the exclamation mark in this sentence:
Why, an orange is orange,
Just an orange!

Words

Write the word that rhymes with:

13 pink _____   **14** blue _____   **15** white _____

Mark your answers. How well did you do?

I scored ____ out of 15.

Here are some things Jasmine wrote about herself.

Me

I am eight years old. I have straight black hair. My eyes are brown. I am quite small for my age. I often wear my favourite green sari. It is soft and shiny. I like school and am a good reader. My worst subject is maths.

My family

I live with my mother and father. I have one older brother called Samir. He is ten. My sister Shirin is younger than me. She is six. My dad works at the airport. My mum stays at home. She looks after us and works very hard. She is a really good cook. I help by doing some of the washing and cooking.

My home

We live in a house. I share a room with my sister. Our front room is full of ornaments. We have a very comfortable leather settee. I love sitting on it, watching TV. Sometimes I play in our garden with my friends. We have a big trampoline in the garden.

My favourite things

I love skipping, reading and playing with friends. My favourite toy is an old teddy bear that I have had since I was a baby. I love bright colourful clothes, and am very fond of shiny hair grips and bracelets.

Checking understanding

Answer these questions.

1. What is the girl's name? _____

2. How many paragraphs is the text divided into? _____

3. Is Jasmine older or younger than Shirin? _____

4. What does Jasmine often wear? _____

5. How many people live in Jasmine's house? _____

6. Where does her dad work? _____

7. What is the front room full of? _____

8. What can Jasmine play on in the garden? _____

9. What is Jasmine's favourite toy? _____

10. What kind of clothes does Jasmine like to wear? _____

Sentences

Fill in each gap with a sensible adjective.

11. Jasmine has _____ eyes.

12. Jasmine's _____ subject is maths.

13. Jasmine is very fond of _____ hair grips.

Words

Fill in the missing letters in these words:

14. fav___ ___rit___

15. c___mf___ ___tab___ ___

Mark your answers. How well did you do?

I scored _____ out of 15.

Once upon a time, elephants had noses instead of trunks. One day, Elephant walked to the green, green river. He saw a log of wood and sat down on it. But then the log opened one eye! Elephant jumped up.

'I'm sorry I sat on you,' he said politely. 'I'm looking for Crocodile. Have you seen him?'

The log of wood opened the other eye. 'Yes. I am Crocodile,' he said. Then Crocodile opened his mouth and laughed. Elephant saw his big, sharp teeth.

Elephant was afraid. 'Ah! I'm glad to meet you,' he said. 'Can I ask you a question?'
'You can,' Crocodile replied.
Elephant said, 'Wh-what do you have for your d-dinner?'
Crocodile laughed again. 'Come closer and I will tell you.'

Elephant walked closer to Crocodile. He put his head right next to Crocodile's mouth so he could hear better.
Crocodile opened his mouth and laughed again. 'I will tell you what I'm going to have for my dinner today,' he said. 'I am going to have – YOU.'

Then Crocodile grabbed Elephant's nose between his teeth – SNAP!
'Let go!' squeaked Elephant.

Elephant pulled one way and Crocodile pulled the other. As they pulled and pulled, Elephant's nose s-t-r-e-t-c-h-e-d into a long trunk. Elephant pulled so hard that Crocodile let go of the elephant's trunk. Elephant fell over backwards with a SPLASH.

Elephant got to his feet and ran away from Crocodile. At last he was free – but now, instead of a nose he had a long trunk.

Adapted from a classic tale by Rudyard Kipling

Checking understanding

Answer these questions with 'yes' or 'no'.

1. In the story, did elephants have noses instead of trunks, once upon a time? _____

2. Did Elephant walk into the desert? _____

3. Did Elephant know the log was Crocodile when he first sat on it? _____

4. Did Crocodile open both eyes at the same time? _____

5. When Crocodile opened his mouth was Elephant frightened? _____

6. Did Crocodile ask Elephant what he had for lunch? _____

7. Did Elephant go closer to Crocodile? _____

8. Did Crocodile grab Elephant's tail? _____

9. When they pulled, did Elephant's nose turn into a long trunk? _____

10. Did Elephant fall forwards with a SPLASH? _____

Sentences

Fill in each gap with a sensible noun.

11. One day, Elephant walked to a green, green _____.

12. When Elephant met Crocodile he said, 'Can I ask you a _____?'

Words

Fill in the missing letters in these words:

13. mou___ ___   14. spla___ ___   15. ele___ ___ant

Mark your answers. How well did you do?

I scored ____ out of 15.

12 Green Lane
Luton
Bedfordshire
LU2 8RZ

23rd August

Dear Gran

Thank you so much for the money you sent me for my birthday. I managed to buy two things I've wanted for a long time. I bought a new pair of trainers because my old ones were very scruffy. Also, I bought a torch so I can read under the covers at night-time.

I had a lovely party. Mum made me a birthday cake. Lots of my friends came. We played pass the parcel and I won the prize. We also played musical statues but I laughed so much I was out first!

Lots of love

Mia xxx

Checking understanding

Answer these questions.

1. What is Mia's address? _____

2. Do you think Mia's birthday is in March or August? _____

3. Who is Mia writing to? _____

4. What did Gran send Mia for her birthday? _____

5. Why did Mia buy a new pair of trainers? _____

6. Why did Mia buy a torch? _____

7. Who did Mia invite to her party? _____

8. Did Mia buy her birthday cake from the shop? _____

9. In which game did Mia win the prize? _____

10. Why was Mia out first when they played musical statues? _____

Sentences

Write each sentence again correctly.

11. mia lives in green lane _____

12. she wrote the letter in august _____

13. luton is a town in bedfordshire _____

Words

14. Find a word containing 'ir': _____

15. Find a word ending with 'el': _____

Mark your answers. How well did you do?

I scored _____ out of 15.

Answers

Test 1

1 a piece of cheese
2 into a tree
3 a hungry fox
4 to make the crow let go of the cheese
5 crafty
6 'What a beautiful bird you are.'
7 'What lovely feathers you've got.'
8 'Have you got a beautiful voice?'
9 The crow wanted to show the fox what a lovely voice she had.
10 She let go of the cheese and it fell to the ground.
11 flew
12 opened
13 piece
14 beautiful
15 laughing

Test 2

1 true
2 false
3 true
4 false
5 true
6 false (it was winter)
7 true
8 true
9 false (they followed Johnny's footprints)
10 true
11 Everywhere he went Johnny planted apple seeds.
12 Did Johnny Appleseed love nature?
13 footprints
14 everywhere
15 sunset

Test 3

1 Betty
2 It was bitter.
3 in her batter
4 Yes
5 It made her batter better.
6 in a flue
7 what they should do
8 'Let us flee!'
9 'Let us fly!'
10 They flew through the flaw in the flue.
11 Betty said, 'My batter is bitter.'
12 The fly said, 'Let us flee!'
13 The flea said, 'Let us fly!'
14 Answers could include: Betty, bought, bit, butter, bitter, batter, better, buy
15 Answers could include: fly, flea, flue, flee, flew, flaw

Test 4

1 cold milk
2 two
3 four
4 Peel the bananas.
5 in the mixing bowl
6 to mash the bananas
7 the milk
8 stir it
9 the ice cream
10 two tall glasses
11 cold

12 medium-sized
13 tall
14 stir
15 serve

Test 5
1 milk
2 grass
3 machine
4 tanker
5 dairy
6 heated up
7 cooled
8 kills
9 cartons
10 shop
11 farmer
12 dairy
13 shop
14 machine
15 plastic

Test 6
1 apples
2 cake
3 ice cream
4 lemon
5 nuts
6 eggs
7 mangoes
8 bananas
9 jelly
10 doughnuts
11 F is for fish, catch it if you can!
12 L is for lemon, too sour by far!
13 apricot, biscuits, crisps
14 fig, grape, jam, melon

15 onion, pear, rice, toast

Test 7
1 draw
2 pencil
3 wood
4 vegetables
5 wheelbarrow
6 king
7 gold
8 rich
9 prison
10 key
11 Chang was a kind boy.
12 Chang saw an old man with a long white beard.
13 straw
14 door
15 road

Test 8
1 yes
2 no
3 yes
4 no
5 yes
6 yes
7 yes
8 no
9 yes
10 no
11 tiny
12 black
13 thick
14 fur
15 tough

Test 9

1 deep
2 splash
3 dry
4 coat
5 wellies
6 boat
7 whoosh
8 black
9 bread
10 bed
11 When it rains it makes puddles.
12 Can I borrow your umbrella?
13 I like deep muddy puddles.
14 sky
15 bed

Test 10

1 shoe shop
2 some new trainers
3 yes (they fitted perfectly)
4 They were worn out.
5 She put on her new trainers.
6 She started to float in the air.
7 smaller
8 beetles
9 ants
10 a little box
11 excited
12 very odd
13 dizzy
14 magic
15 excited

Test 11

1 true
2 false
3 true
4 false
5 false
6 true
7 true
8 false
9 true
10 false
11 Cara said, 'Look! I can swim underwater!'
12 'Watch me jump the waves!' Alfie shouted.
13 Cara said, 'The sun will soon dry our clothes.'
14 peach
15 wrong

Test 12

1 Andy Hay
2 in the big blue bay
3 a shark
4 It ate him.
5 Algy
6 a bear
7 It ate him.
8 bananas
9 on an elephant's toe
10 'Why don't you pick on somebody your own size?'
11 Andy went for a swim in the bay.
12 A grasshopper stood on an elephant's toe.
13 grasshopper
14 bear
15 shark

Test 13

1 in the kitchen
2 a dragon
3 sharp and pointed
4 smoke
5 some eggs
6 swallowed a whole tin (in one mouthful)
7 the whole loaf
8 a loud hiss
9 his wings
10 where the dragon was going for lunch
11 long
12 deep
13 open
14 whales
15 cloud

Test 14

1 on the floor
2 the gate
3 your lips
4 your shoe
5 your spine
6 your knee
7 you learn to jive
8 up to heaven
9 Number one, stick out your tongue.
10 ten
11 Number one, stick out your tongue.
12 Number ten, do it again!
13 shoe
14 floor
15 gate

Test 15

1 true
2 true
3 false
4 false
5 true
6 false
7 true
8 false
9 true
10 true
11 grow
12 carry
13 eat
14 branches
15 leaves

Test 16

1 Thunderbolt
2 barrel
3 stuck
4 beard
5 left
6 short
7 timber
8 frightening
9 sword
10 night
11 captain
12 scarf
13 harbour
14 pirate
15 sword

Test 17

1 rose
2 poppy

3 clouds
4 sailing
5 Pears
6 flowers
7 twilight
8 orange
9 Eight
10 seventeen
11 What is orange?
12 Why, an orange is orange,
   Just an orange!
13 brink
14 through
15 light

Test 18
1 Jasmine
2 four
3 older
4 a green sari
5 five
6 at the airport
7 ornaments
8 a trampoline
9 an old teddy bear
10 bright colourful clothes
11 brown
12 worst
13 shiny
14 favourite
15 comfortable

Test 19
1 yes

2 no
3 no
4 no
5 yes
6 no (he asked what he had for his
   dinner)
7 yes
8 no
9 yes
10 no (he fell backwards)
11 river
12 question
13 mouth
14 splash
15 elephant

Test 20
1 12 Green Lane, Luton,
   Bedfordshire, LU2 8RZ
2 August
3 Gran
4 some money
5 her old ones were scruffy
6 so she could read under the
   covers at night-time
7 lots of friends
8 no, her mum made it
9 pass the parcel
10 because she laughed so much
11 Mia lives in Green Lane.
12 She wrote the letter in August.
13 Luton is a town in Bedfordshire.
14 birthday
15 parcel